Company's Coming

A Passover Lift-the-Flap Book

written by Joan Holub • *illustrated by* Renée Andriani

PUFFIN BOOKS

Company's coming.
It's Passover night.
I help set the table.
Now it's just right.

First in English,
and then in Hebrew.

We have our freedom, so let's celebrate
with six special foods from the Seder plate.

Please pass the chicken
and matzoh ball soup,
gefilte fish, and a
chopped liver scoop.

Dad hides the matzoh. We try not to peek.

Now that it's hidden, it's time to go seek.

Open the door
so Elijah will come.
Mama pours the wine.
Do you think he'll
drink some?

Dinner is over.
The meal has been long.
But there is still time
for dessert and a song.

GLOSSARY

Afikomen (ah-fee-KO-men): A piece of matzoh that is broken and hidden for children to find during the Seder.

Elijah (ee-LIE-juh): A Hebrew prophet who will foretell the coming of the Messiah.

Four Questions: The youngest person at the Seder asks the leader four important questions about Passover. The first one is, Why is this night different from all other nights?

Gefilte fish (gah-FIL-tah fish): Fish balls made from chopped fish, onions, matzoh meal, eggs, and spices.

Haggadah (hah-GAH-dah): A book about Passover that is read at the Seder.

Haroset (hah-RO-set): A mixture of nuts, fruit, wine, and spices that symbolizes the mortar and bricks the Hebrews used to build when they were slaves in Egypt.

Matzoh (MAHT-za): A crackerlike bread that does not contain yeast.

Passover: A holiday in the spring celebrating the Hebrews' freedom from slavery in Egypt long ago.

Seder (SAY-dur): A ceremony and dinner on the first two nights of Passover.

Seder plate: A plate that holds the six special foods at the Seder: bitter herbs and vegetables, parsley, haroset, lamb bone, and egg.